THE WEAPONS EN[...]

TANK AIRCRAFT AFV SHIP ARTILLERY VEHICLES SECRET WEAPON

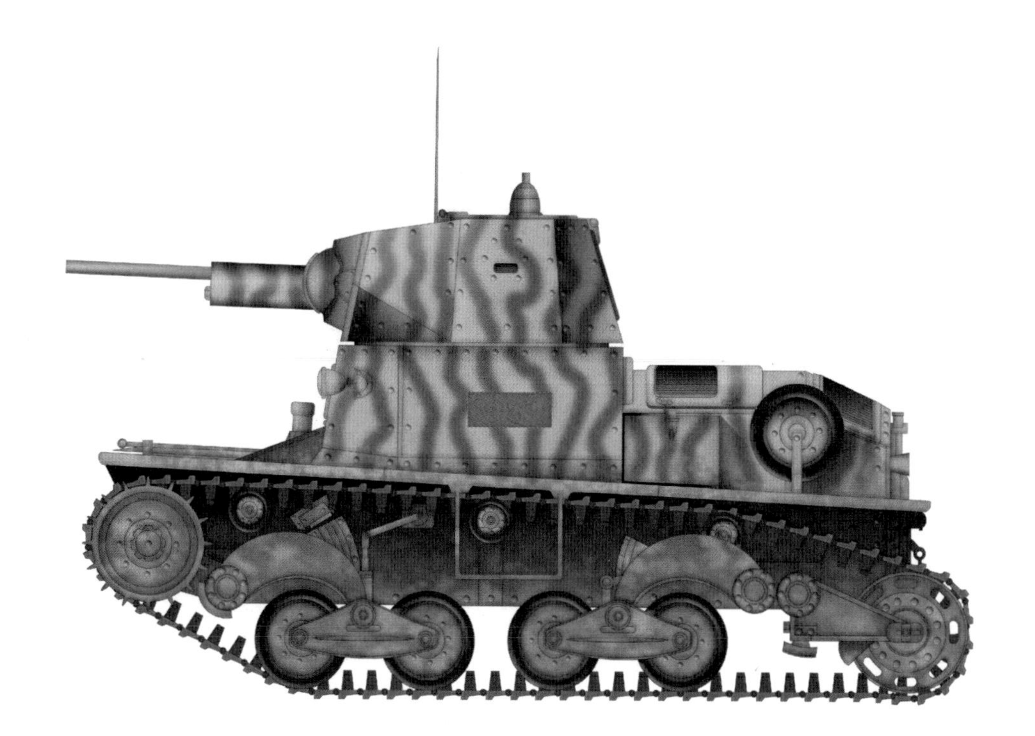

LIGHT TANK L6/40

THE WEAPONS ENCICLOPÆDIA

EDITORIAL STAFF

Luca Cristini, Paolo Crippa.

REDAZIONE ACCADEMICA

Enrico Acerbi, Massimiliano Afiero, Aldo Antonicelli, Ruggero Calò, Luigi Carretta, Flavio Chistè, Anna Cristini, Carlo Cucut, Salvo Fagone, Enrico Finazzer, Björn Huber, Andrea Lombardi, Aymeric Lopez, Marco Lucchetti, Luigi Manes, Giovanni Maressi, Francesco Mattesini, Federico Peirani, Alberto Peruffo, Maurizio Raggi, Andrea Alberto Tallillo, Antonio Tallillo, Massimo Zorza.

PUBLISHED BY

Luca Cristini Editore (Soldiershop), via Orio, 33/D - 24050 Zanica (BG) ITALY.

DISTRIBUTION BY

Soldiershop - www.soldiershop.com, Amazon, Ingram Spark, Berliner Zinnfigurem (D), LaFeltrinelli, Mondadori, Libera Editorial (Spain).

CONTRIBUTORS OF THIS VOLUME & ACKNOWLEDGEMENTS

Ringraziamo i principali collaboratori di questo numero: I profili dei carri sono tutti dell'autore. Le colorazioni delle foto sono di Anna Cristini. Ringraziamenti particolari a istituzioni nazionali e/o private quali: Stato Maggiore dell'esercito, Archivio di Stato, Bundesarchiv, Nara, Library of Congress ecc. A P.Crippa, A.Lopez, L.Manes, C.Cucut, archivi Tallillo. Model Victoria (www.modelvictoria.it), per avere messo a disposizione immagini o altro dei loro archivi.

For a complete list of Soldiershop titles, or for every information please contact us on our website: www.soldiershop.com or www.cristinieditore.com. E-mail: info@soldiershop.com. Keep up to date on Facebook & Twitter: https://www.facebook.com/soldiershop.publishing

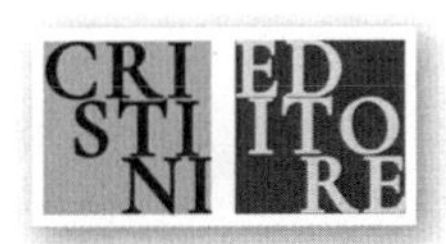

Title: **ITALIAN LIGHT TANK L6/40** Code.: **TWE-010 EN**
Series by L. S. Cristini
ISBN code: 978-88-93279710 1st edition June 2023
THE WEAPONS ENCICLOPAEDIA (SOLDIERSHOP) is a trademark of Luca Cristini Editore.

THE WEAPONS ENCYCLOPÆDIA

TANK AIRCRAFT AFV SHIP ARTILLERY VEHICLES SECRET WEAPON

ITALIAN LIGHT TANK L6/40

LUCA STEFANO CRISTINI

BOOK SERIES FOR MODELERS & COLLECTORS

CONTENTS

▼ L6/40 tank in winter camouflage for Russia. Wikipedia

INTRODUCTION

Since the L3 tanks, disparagingly referred to as 'sardine cans', were already anachronistic in the second half of the 1930s, the Italian High Command sought to develop a new light tank to replace these crawlers, whose main defect (the armoured superstructure and lack of a turret) had already been well revealed during the Ethiopian War.

The only true Italian light tank of the Second World War can therefore be defined as the L6/40. It was used during the conflict, mainly by the Regio Esercito, which employed it in all theatres of war, mainly as a reconnaissance vehicle from the spring of 1941 until the Armistice with the Allies in September 1943. Originally designed for mountain operations, it soon proved unsuitable for operations in North Africa or Russia. Even before it went into action, it was obsolete both in terms of armament and weak armour.
It was the only light tank in the Italian Army equipped with a turret. It always provided very mediocre evidence as an armoured vehicle and ended up performing, at least in North Africa, support duties for Italian infantry attacks in the vast desert spaces.

DEVELOPMENT AND PRODUCTION

The first evolution of the L3 Model 36 tank was produced in November 1935 in prototype form; it retained the lower chassis and engine compartment of its predecessor, while benefiting from a more spacious superstructure and turret armament consisting of a 37 mm cannon coupled to a 6.5 mm machine gun. The gearbox suspension was torsion bar suspension, a solution that was also retained in the future L6/40. The latter was initially conceived with the outdated view of use mainly in the mountains, in memory of the

▲ Prototype tank mod. 36 seen from the front. Aymeric Lopez collection. Author's colouring.

▲ Some of the main tank designs/prototypes presented by Ansaldo E Fiat in the courtyard of a cavalry barracks in the mid-1930s. From left to right: an L3/33 light fast tank, in the middle behind the two soldiers the 1936 *Model Cannon Tank* (predecessor of our L6/40) finally on the right the 10t *Breaking Tank* (prototype M11/39).

conflict that the Royal Italian Army fought against the Austro-Hungarian Empire on Italy's north-eastern border. This mountainous terrain was particularly suitable for 3-tonne light tanks. Obviously, this basic principle soon proved to be useless and misleading. For this reason, a cannon in the rotating turret was not subsequently considered. In a mountainous front it was virtually impossible to be outflanked by the enemy, and having a piece in a rigid casemate firing forward was more than sufficient.

These considerations, coupled with the L3's poor performance in the recent war in Ethiopia, prompted the Royal Italian Army to pursue the study of a new light tank equipped with a turret and armed with a cannon. FIAT of Turin and Ansaldo of Genoa began a joint project for the new tank using the L3/35 chassis, the latest evolution of the L3 tank series, as the basis. In November 1935, they presented the Model 1936 Assault Tank, with the same chassis and engine compartment as the L3/35 3-tonne tank, but with new torsion bar suspension, a modified superstructure and a turret with 37 mm cannon. Initial tests were carried out at Ansaldo's facilities; the prototype was then sent to the Centro Studi della Motorizzazione (or CSM) in Rome. The CSM was the Italian department in charge of examining new vehicles for the Regio Esercito.

During these tests, the prototype of the 1936 Model Assault Tank achieved mixed results: the new suspension gave a good impression, while the vehicle's lack of stability, especially when firing, quickly became a problem. Because of this, the Royal Army requested a new design.

► The prototype of the 1936 Model Cannon Tank photographed outside the Ansaldo factories. (Ansaldo source).

▲ The prototype of the L4 light tank during the first tests. Designed for the mountain front, the Regio Esercito General Staff tested it on the paths of Alpine villages as you can see in the large photo. (Ansaldo source).

▲ The 1936 *Model assault tank* during testing at the Centro Studi della Motorizzazione in Rome. 12 November 1935. Source: Centro Tecnico della Motorizzazione Esercito Italiano.

In April 1936, the same two companies presented the new Model 1936 tank, this time different from the old L3/35 progenitor. The new prototype was equipped with a 37 mm cannon on the left side of the superstructure, with limited translation and a revolving turret armed with a pair of machine guns. However, the Royal Army criticised these choices made by the two companies, simply because this was not the tank that the General Staff had requested.

The M6 prototype

The two Italian companies did not give up, however, and designed a new prototype based on a rotating turret and new suspension. To strengthen their position, Ansaldo and FIAT also spread the rumour of some interest in the vehicle from a foreign power. Only towards the end of 1937, following administrative delays, was the prototype ready. Armed with no less than two machine guns in the turret, it was first christened M6 (Medium Tank), later corrected to L6 (L stands for Light) following Circular No. 1400 of 13 June 1940, which raised the category limit for medium tanks from 5 tonnes to 8 tonnes. The FIAT and Ansaldo prototype was eventually presented to the generals of the Army General Staff at Villa Glori on 26 October 1939. This time, too, the General Staff turned their thumbs down. However, General Manera of the Motorisation Study Centre ended up accepting it with reservation on condition that the turret armament was changed. There were still a number of mishaps and accidents, but eventually, after a new series of tests between 1939 and 1940, the *L6/40 Tank was* officially born in April of the latter year, short for: *6-ton Light Tank Model 1940.*

Production

An important point to clarify was which armament would be chosen, as FIAT-Ansaldo had not yet received any information on which model the Regio Esercito wanted, the 20 mm cannon or the 37 mm cannon. On 18 March 1940, the Regio Esercito placed its first order for 583 M6 vehicles, together with M13/40 tanks and other armoured cars. The contract specified a requirement for at least 480 light tanks per year, numbers that were impossible at the time for Italian industry, which was barely able to produce around 80 per cent of them. The first delivery took place in late May 1941, behind schedule and with the war already on! In the meantime, the order had changed, and more models of L40 self-propelled vehicles were requested than tanks. In the end, 414 L6/40s came out of the FIAT factories in Turin. The fledgling tank was already old and General Roatta, who had no confidence in the vehicle, asked that production be stopped at 100 vehicles, but the assembly line was now operational. In any case, the army and manufacturers agreed to cease production in December 1943. Obviously the Armistice accelerated this situation and by 8 September the total number produced was 416 tanks. The Germans took over the factories and, under their direction, other vehicles were produced and by the end of 1944, a total of 432 L6/40 light tanks were produced.

TECHNICAL SPECIFICATIONS

The tank consists of the chassis or hull, the armament, the engine and the associated transmission, locomotion and control organs. These are the main parts: hull - accesses - inspection hatches - exhaust ports - means of visibility - engine - transmission organs - steering and braking organs - external propulsion and suspension organs.

Armour

The front plates that formed the structure of the vehicle were 30 mm thick, while those of the gun shield and driver's hatch were thicker, reaching 40 mm. Much lighter were the plates defending the transmission compartment and the side plates, and the rear plates were 15 mm thick. The bottom/floor of the tank

▲ Cross-section of the L6/40 tank from the original Fiat maintenance booklet.

was 10 mm thick. So not only was the thickness poor, but the quality of the steel also left much to be desired. The Italian industry was unable to supply sufficient quantities for the armour of the tanks, as the steel was assigned to the Regia Marina. This got worse and worse and reached its peak during the wars in Ethiopia and Spain. The armour of the L6/40s often proved puncturable even by small-calibre shells and most anti-tank guns. According to the Italian tradition, the armour was all bolted on, certainly not the best technology existing at the time, indeed already surpassed by the safer welding. However, this was a forced choice for Italian production, as bolts offered the advantage of making the manufacturing process easier and faster than welded armour.

Hull and combat chamber

At the front of the vehicle was the transmission cover, with a large inspection hatch that could be opened by the driver via an internal lever. This was often left open to cool the internal mechanisms. A shovel and crowbar were located on the right wing, while a rounded jack stand was on the left. The vehicle had swivelling headlights mounted on the sides of the vehicle. The driver was positioned on the right and had a hatch that could be opened by a lever mounted on the right. He also had at his disposal a 190 x 36 episcope with a horizontal field of view of 30° and a vertical one of 8°. On his left the driver had the gear lever and hand brake, while on the right was the dashboard. Under the driver's seat were the 12V *Magneti Marelli* batteries that were used to start the engine and power the vehicle's electrical systems. In the centre of the fighting chamber was the drive shaft that connected the engine to the transmission. Due to the limited space inside, the vehicle was not equipped with an intercom system, so the crew communicated by direct voice. A large tank with engine cooling water was located at the rear of the combat chamber and in the middle was a fire extinguisher. On the sides were two air intakes to allow ventilation inside the

▲ The inside of the combat chamber, legend: 1 Turret rotation device. 2 Headset and intercom attachment. 3 Pilot-servant seat. 4 Magazine compartments for 20 mm weapon shells. 5 Tank radio equipment. 6 Fire extinguisher. / Pedals to operate the tank's weapons control (cannon and machine gun). Source A. Lopez.

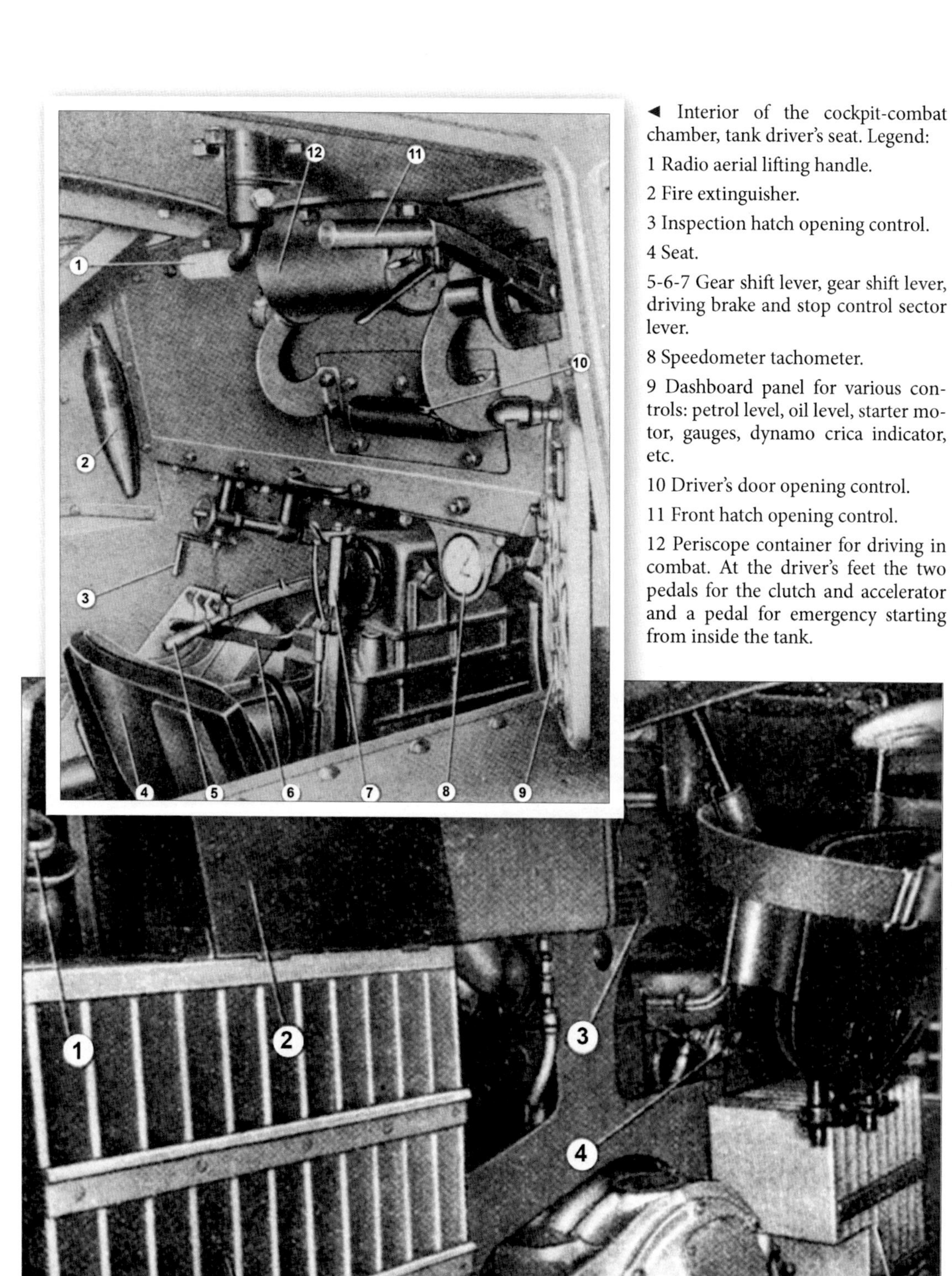

◄ Interior of the cockpit-combat chamber, tank driver's seat. Legend:

1 Radio aerial lifting handle.

2 Fire extinguisher.

3 Inspection hatch opening control.

4 Seat.

5-6-7 Gear shift lever, gear shift lever, driving brake and stop control sector lever.

8 Speedometer tachometer.

9 Dashboard panel for various controls: petrol level, oil level, starter motor, gauges, dynamo crica indicator, etc.

10 Driver's door opening control.

11 Front hatch opening control.

12 Periscope container for driving in combat. At the driver's feet the two pedals for the clutch and accelerator and a pedal for emergency starting from inside the tank.

▲ Combat chamber rear wall. Legend: 1 Engine cooling water inlet. 2 Optical parts box. 3 Fuel tank use plate. 4 Fuel tap. 5 Bullet magazine compartments. Source A.Lopez.

vehicle when all hatches were closed. On the bulkhead, above the propeller shaft, there were two opening inspection doors to the engine compartment. The engine and crew compartments were in turn separated by an armoured bulkhead, which served to protect the men from the risk of fire spreading into the combat chamber. The engine was located in the centre of the rear compartment, next to two fuel tanks of 83 litres each. Behind the engine were the radiator and the lubricating oil tank. The engine compartment had two large doors with two grilles for cooling the engine and, behind, two air intakes for the radiator. It was not uncommon for the crew to travel with all the hatches open during North African operations to better ventilate the engine and interior, due to the high temperatures. Finally, the muffler was located on the right rear wall of the mudguards. On the first vehicles produced, this still lacked an adequate asbestos cover. The rear part of the engine compartment had a removable round plate attached with bolts and used for engine maintenance. On the left side was a pick holder and the plate with the red stop light.

Engine and suspension

The engine of the L6/40 light tank was the *FIAT-SPA Type 18VT* petrol-driven, liquid-cooled, 4-cylinder in-line engine with a maximum output of 68 hp at 2,500 rpm. It had a volume of 4,053 cm^3. The same engine was also used on the self-propelled versions derived from the L6 tank. This engine, in turn, was derived from the one used on some 55 hp military truck models, but was in an upgraded version. The engine of the L6 tank could be started electrically or manually via a crank that had to be inserted in the rear. The Zenith Type 42 TTVP carburettor was the same one used on the AB series medium armoured cars and allowed ignition even when cold. The two tanks with a total capacity of 165 litres ensured a range of 200 km on the road and about 5 hours off-road, with a maximum speed of 42 km/h on the road and 20-25 km/h on rough terrain, depending on the terrain on which the light reconnaissance tank had to operate. The L6 tank could carry a maximum of five additional canisters of 20 litres each for a total of

▲ Right side of Engine FIAT-SPA Type 18VT FIAT-Ansaldo Mod. L6. From Operation and Maintenance Manual.

100 litres of fuel, three on the left side of the superstructure and one above each rear wing toolbox. These additional canisters increased the vehicle's maximum range to around 320 km. The transmission had a single dry plate clutch. The gearbox had 4 forward and 1 reverse gear with a speed reducer. The gearbox gearing consisted of a 16-tooth front sprocket, four coupled road wheels, three upper rollers and a rear idler wheel on each side. The swing arms were attached to the sides of the chassis and were connected to torsion bars. The tracks were derived from those of the L3 series light tanks and consisted of 88 links 260 mm wide on each side. The L6/40's engine suffered when starting at low temperatures, something suffered especially by the crews deployed in Russia: FIAT developed a preheating system to reduce this inconvenience.

Turret and armament

The L6/40 turret was developed by Ansaldo and assembled by SPA for the L6/40 light tank and also used on the AB41 armoured car. The single-seat turret had an octagonal shape with two hatches: one for the vehicle commander/cannon on the roof and the second at the rear of the turret, used to remove the main armament during maintenance operations. On the sides, the turret had two loopholes to allow commanders to check the battlefield and use their personal weapons, with not a few difficulties given the cramped space. On the roof, next to the hatch, was a periscope with a field of view of 30°, which allowed the commander too partial a view of the battlefield because it was impossible, again due to the limited space, to rotate it 360°. The commander's position in the turret was problematic and he had to sit on a folding seat. The commanders were also responsible for firing the guns, and operated the cannon and machine gun using foot pedals because, in the absence of electric generators, one had to act mechanically, pulling metal cables similar to those on bicycle brakes. The commander also had a radio at his disposal, a *Magneti Marelli RF1CA-TR7* transceiver with an operating frequency range of 27 to 33.4 MHz. connected to 12V batteries manufactured by *Magneti Marelli*. This radio had two ranges, a near range with a maximum range of 5 km, and a far range with a maximum range of 12 km. The radio weighed about 13 kg and was placed on the left side of the superstructure. The mobile antenna was located on the right

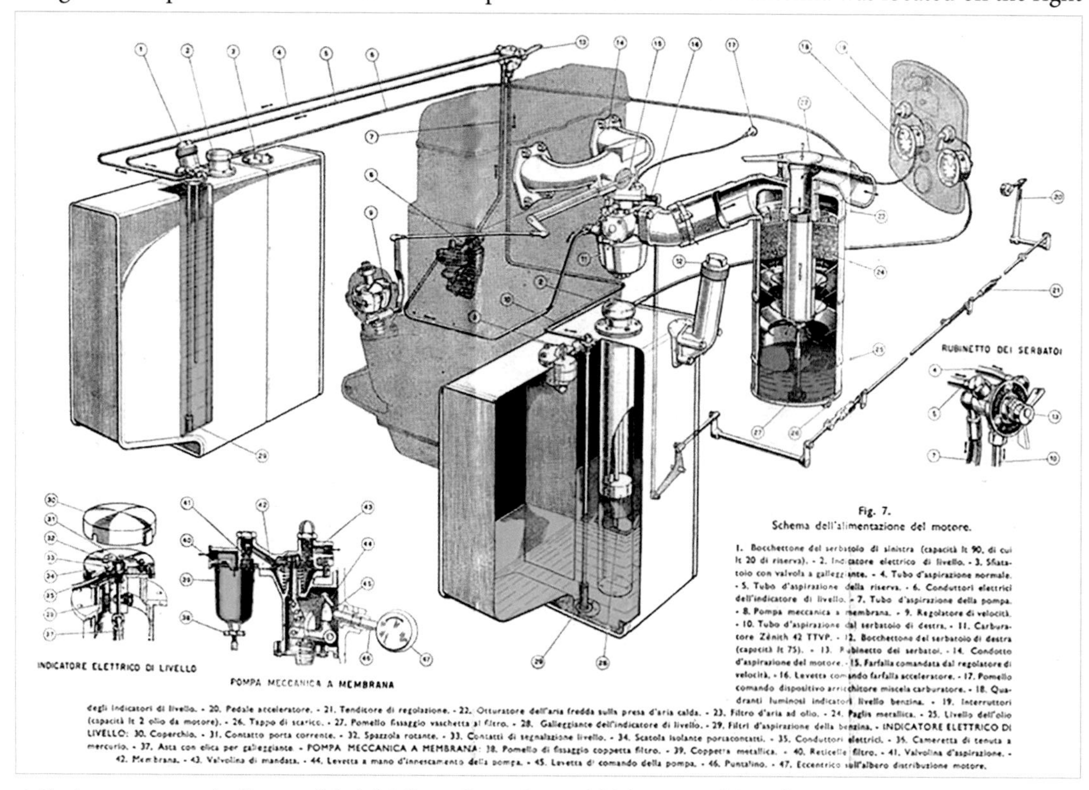

▲ Engine power supply diagram. Mod. L6. From Operation and Maintenance Manual.

side of the roof and could be lowered 90° backwards with a crank operated by the driver. The tank's main weapon was a *Breda 20/65 Model 1935* air-cooled gas *gun* developed by the *Società Italiana Ernesto Breda per Costruzioni Meccaniche* of Brescia. It was, in fact, a cannon designed as an anti-aircraft and anti-tank gun and was even adopted for some variants of the German Panzer I in Spain. The cannon was a good weapon, appreciated even by the enemies who captured many of them in Africa following the collapse of the Axis troops. The automatic cannon weighed 307 kg with an elevation of +80°. Its maximum range was 5,500 m. Against airborne aircraft it had a practical range of 1,500 metres, while against armoured targets it only had a chance of doing harm if the target was between 600 and 1,000 metres maximum. In the tank version, the Breda gun was fed by 8-round magazines, due to the limited space available inside the vehicle turrets. However, the firing rate was also limited due to the fact that the commander/cannon fighter was alone and had to open fire and reload the main gun. The secondary armament consisted, as with many other Italian tanks, of an 8mm *Breda Model 1938* mounted coaxially to the cannon, on the left, with a maximum weight of 20 kg and a theoretical rate of fire of 450 rounds per minute. In time, Breda developed a version of the machine gun suitable for tanks. This was lighter, with a shortened barrel, pistol grip and a new 24-round curved upper magazine. The weapon was renowned for its robustness and accuracy, but it also had an annoying tendency to jam easily and a prohibitive weight compared to similar weapons used by the enemy (15 to 19 kg... a huge amount).

▲ FIAT advertising image showing an SPA worker finishing assembling the gun of an L6/40.

Crew and tactical organisation

The crew of the L6/40 consisted of only two soldiers. The driver placed to the right of the vehicle and the commander/cannoneer just behind, both sitting on a seat attached to the turret ring. The commanders, as already mentioned, had to perform too many tasks and this was perhaps the main Achilles heel of the vehicle's effectiveness. They were also forced to check the battlefield, locate targets, open fire, give orders to the driver, use the tank's radio station and load both the automatic cannon and the machine gun... just too much. Similar vehicles, such as the German Panzer II, had a crew of three and it was a different story.

The L6/40 squadrons consisted of a *command platoon*, four tank platoons plus one in reserve/depot, giving a total per squadron of seven officers, 26 non-commissioned officers, 135 soldiers, 28 L6/40 light tanks and other support vehicles. In June 1942, the battalions, or L6 groups, were reorganised into a command platoon with two L6/40 command tanks and two L6/40 radio tanks, and two to three tank companies, each with 27 L6 light tanks.

VERSIONS OF THE VEHICLES

The L6/40 light tank had a production run of only a few variants, excluding the initial prototypes intended for design. Here are the main production or modified and derived versions:

- **L6/40** – the L6/40 in its basic version was not a great success with the crews. General Gervasio Bitossi, commander of the Littorio Division, who also commanded the 3rd Armoured Group Novara, complained first of all about its main armament and its short range, which made it far from ideal for long-range reconnaissance missions, and also about its speed, considered too low for missions of this type. To make matters worse, the L6/40 had a tendency to sink in sandy terrain and the specific resistance of the delicate torsion bars was a problem that plagued the tank all too often. The tank's excessively high silhouette (despite being a light tank) made it highly visible to enemy observers from afar. On paper, the vehicle was compared to the German Panzer II, but on the German vehicle, a three-man crew operated, while on the L6/40, the tank commander operated alone in the turret and also had to perform the work of a gunner and radio operator.
- **L6/40LF** – version with a flamethrower instead of a cannon, equipped with a 200-litre liquid fuel tank. The flamethrower version was developed on the basis of the RE 3812 tank in December 1941. After evaluation tests conducted by the CSM in the summer of 1942, the L40 LF was adopted on 1 September of the same year. The flamethrower tube, built on the same model as that installed on the L3 LF, occupied the place of the 20 mm cannon. Probably only the prototype was made, although some sources claim that a small batch of these tanks was produced and it cannot be ruled out that some were sent to the Balkans. Weighing 7 tonnes, this armour carried 200 litres of flammable liquid.

▲ The final M6 prototype just off the assembly line, ready to be tested. Note the absence of the episcope support. Source: Ansaldo. Author's colouring.

- **L6/40 Radio Centre** – radio tank used as a command vehicle, with open turret and improved means of communication with additional equipment, remained at the prototype stage.
- **L6/40 Ammunition Carrier** – ammunition carrier that accompanied the M.41 90/53 self-propelled vehicles; carried 26 rounds on board and 40 on an armoured trailer.

Main modified or derived versions:

- **L40** – an abbreviation of the full **L40 47/32** self-propelled gun, was an artillery and tank destroyer self-propelled gun made by the usual FIAT-SPA consortium and Ansaldo for the Regio Esercito. Developed from the L6/40, whose turret was removed to make room for a 47/32 Mod. 1935 47 mm anti-tank gun.
- **Command Tank L40** - command tank for self-propelled platoon and company. Developed in two variants: self-propelled platoon command tank and self-propelled squadron/company command tank. Equipped with additional radio equipment, the cannon was replaced by an 8 mm Breda Mod. 38 machine gun, the barrel of which was, however, encased in a wider sleeve, so that the vehicle externally appeared the same as the others, in order to confuse the enemy. After the armistice, this version was also heavily employed by the Wehrmacht under the new name PzBefWg L6 770(i).
- **Cingoletta L40** – the Italian counterpart of the British Universal Carrier, which however remained only at prototype level.

L6/40 Tank **Production**			
Year	**First batch registration number**	**Last batch registration number**	**Total**
1941	3.808	3.881	71
1942	3.882	5.470	330
1943	5.481	5.508	14
	Total Italian production		415
1943-44	**German Production**		17
Total	415+17		432

▲ View of the M6 prototype during its official presentation by Ansaldo (State Archives).

► The final outline of the L6/40 in Imperial camouflage at the Ansaldo-Fossati plant in Sestri Ponente. Paolo Crippa Collection.

► L6/40 ammunition carrier version. The vehicle was designed to supply the 90/53 Semovente heavy fighters. The vehicle could carry 26 projectiles of 90 mm calibre and a further 40 projectiles could be transported in the ammunition trailer. Thirty of these vehicles were produced, one for each tank destroyer.

▼ L6 command tank radio centre of the LXVIIth Bersaglieri Battalion at Iagodniy in Russia 27 August 1942. Collection A.Lopez.

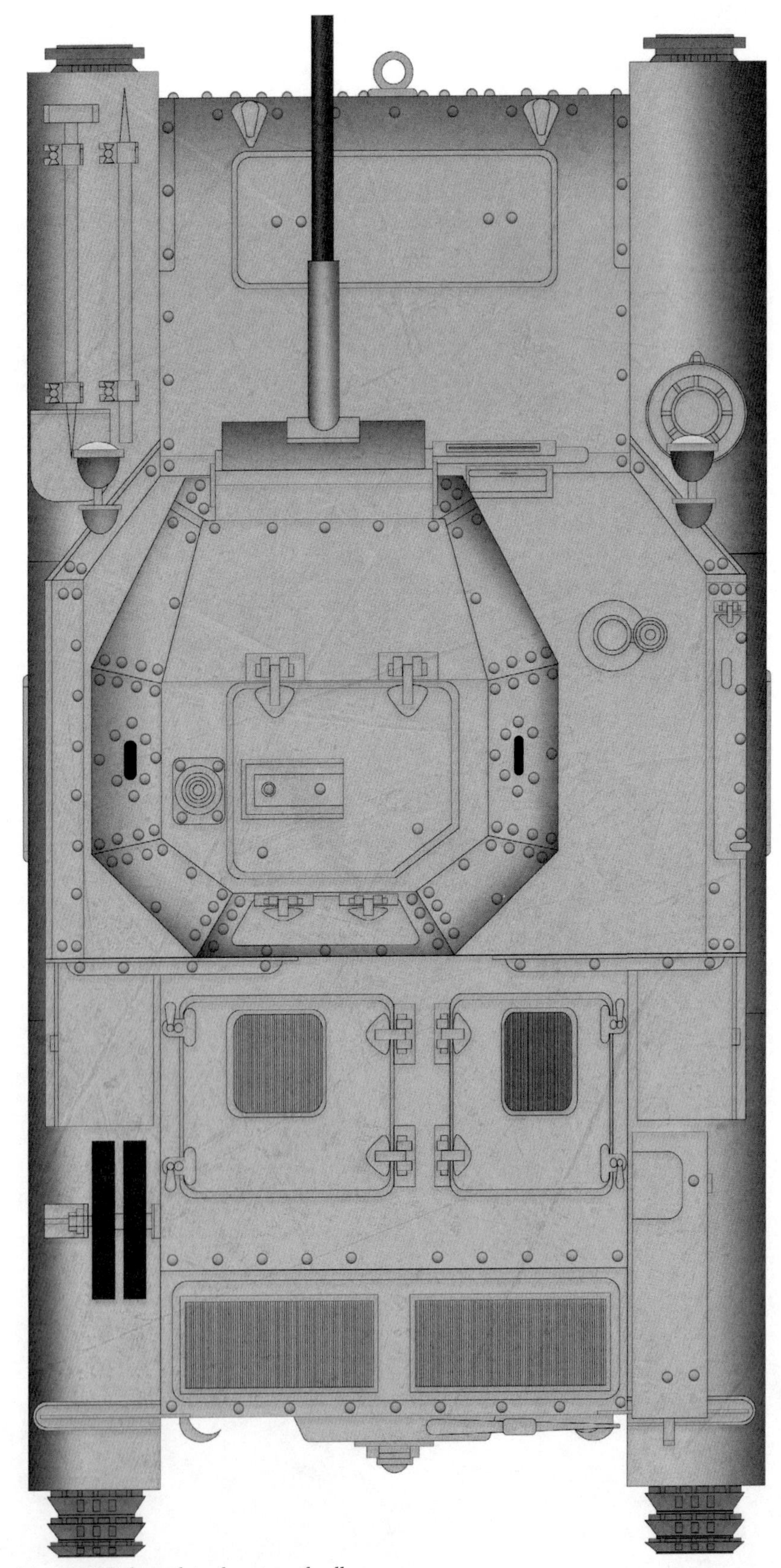

▲ Top view of the L6/40 light tank in desert sand yellow.

L6/40 LIGHT TANK NORTH AFRICA CAMPAIGN

▲ L6/40 tank 2nd Company III Squadron of the 5th Novara Lancers Regiment. Littorio Division. Fouka, Libya, June 1942.

The Italian Bren Carrier

The idea of a reconnaissance and transport crawler, similar to the British Bren Carrier, was developed by Ansaldo as early as 1938, with the creation of an open-top prototype, based on the mechanics of the future L6/40 tank, capable of carrying up to seven men, ammunition and spare parts, or towing artillery pieces. However, the revolutionary idea came too late, with the war already lost. The design of the Italian light crawler was assigned to engineer Rosini of Ansaldo, who christened the vehicle the CVP/5. In 1942, the General Staff approved the design, which, however, never went into production due to the African reverses at the end of the year.

► Front view of the Italian 'Bren Carrier' CVP/5, which never reached prototype level due to Italian military disasters on the various fronts..

► View of the L6/40 flamethrower version, with the tube instead of the 1941 cannon.

▼ Nice close-up of the light tank. It did indeed look like a successful vehicle, which unfortunately appeared too late.

Source: P. Crippa

L6/40 LIGHT TANK RUSSIAN CAMPAIGN

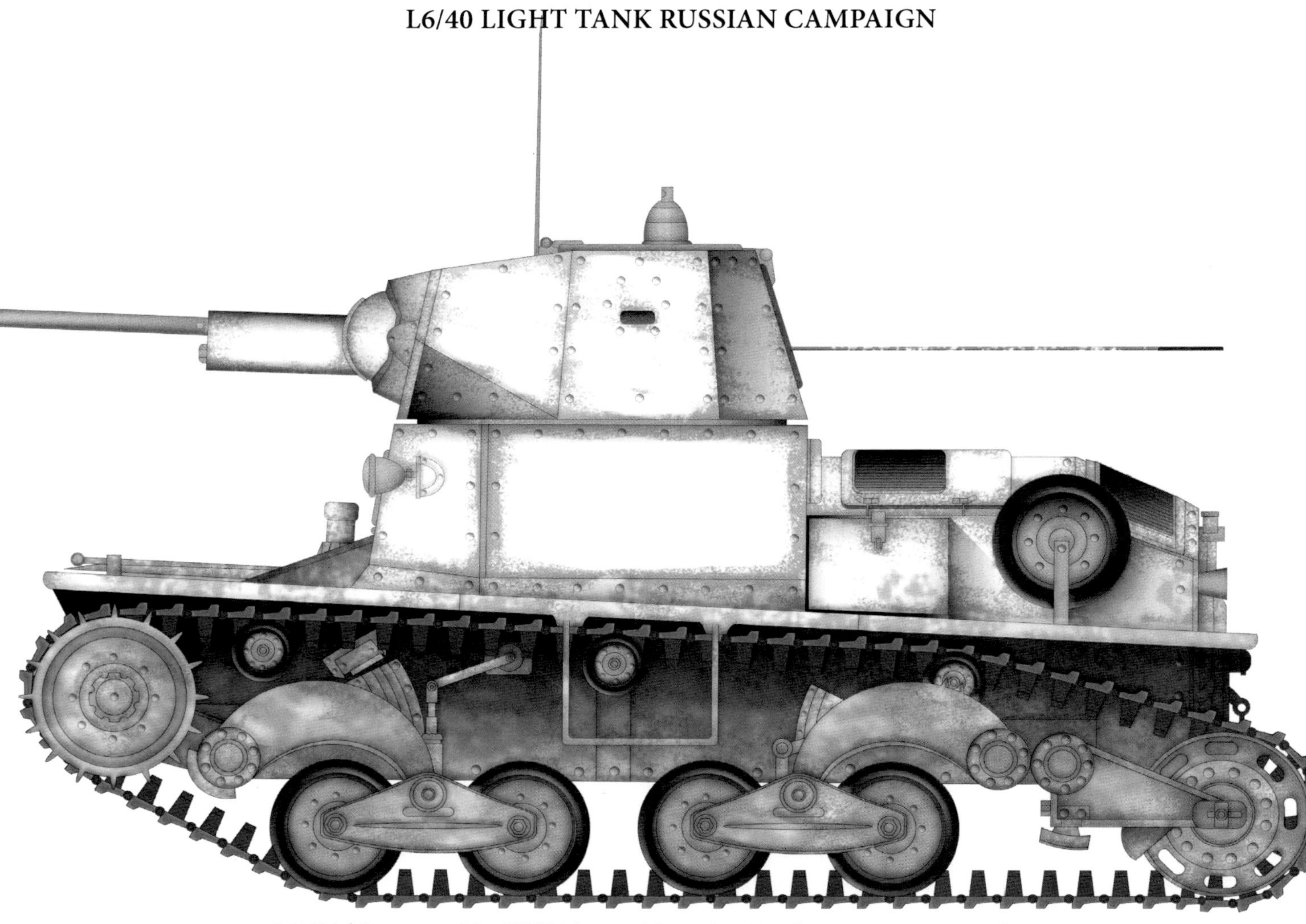

▲ L6/40 2nd Company of the LXVII Motorised Bersaglieri Battalion. Don Front, September 1942.

47-32 SELF-PROPELLED TANK LIBYA CAMPAIGN

▲ 47-32 Semovente employed in the Cyrenaean desert. Libya, 1942.

OPERATIONAL USE

Although in many respects an efficient vehicle in its class, the L6/40 was generally considered an 'old' vehicle, both in terms of armament and armour. It failed to adequately fulfil the roles for which it was created, namely reconnaissance and infantry support. Moreover, the L6/40 tank was also used as a breakout tank for lack of more suitable vehicles, which was absurd for such a poorly armoured tank. With regard to the other roles for which it was conceived, i.e. reconnaissance and infantry support, it was partially suited to the former because it was fast and small, while it was unlikely to be able to fulfil the latter, also because it was penalised by the employment doctrine in use at the time in the Regio Esercito. The operational life of the L6/40 was relatively short and concentrated in the period of greatest Italian war effort between the end of 1941 and 1943. The vehicle was mainly assigned to the fast troops (Cavalry and Bersaglieri), effectively equipping squadron/company-level units, with the exception of those assigned to the III Armoured Group 'Lancieri di Novara'.
The vehicles were used by the Regio Esercito in practically every front of the Second World War where Italian forces were involved: in North Africa, on the Eastern Front in Russia with the ARMIR, in the Balkans with tasks to counter Yugoslav resistance operations. Some of these were then captured and reused by the Germans after 8 September 1943, and later also by the Tito partisans, and, of course, the vehicles that remained in Italy after the armistice were also reused by the German armed forces; only a very limited number of those that remained in Italy could be used by the units of the RSI. Starting in 1943, the tank turret was also used on the SPA-Viberti AS43 armoured car. The Italian Army continued to use the L6/40s that had survived the conflict until the early 1950s, as did the Rapid Units of the Public Security Service.

▼ L6/40 tank of the 2nd Battalion of the 31st Tank Regiment engaged in the recovery of a German truck. Note the lion's head painted on the front of the casemate and the white rectangles, long side up, typical of the tanks of this unit that supported the German armed forces after the Armistice. (Author's colouring).

NORTH AFRICAN FRONT

The first 4 L6/40s sent to North Africa in December 1941, after the war had already begun, were trained in an experimental platoon of the Nice Training Company, attached to RECAM (Reconnaissance Group of the Army Manoeuvre Corps). From the end of January 1942, the 3rd Armoured Group of the Cavalry Regiment I Lancieri di Novara, formed in Verona, began to receive the first L6s. On 4 March 1942, this unit reached Africa and became part of the 133ª Littorio Armoured Division. It became operational with a strength of 85 L6s (Bizzarri says 52). Other groups of the same unit operated on the Russian front together with the Savoy Cavalry Regiment. The unit took part in the attacks on Tobruk, and was later placed at Rommel's disposal. It then fought at El-Adem and in early July took part in the first battle of El Alamein.

On the eve of the Third Battle of El Alamein, the 3rd Armoured Group Novara had only 24 operational L6s. The last five tanks of this group were abandoned in the El Daba logistics depot during the retreat from El Alamein (including the one with the number 3700, now on display in the Egyptian memorial).

The 2nd Squadron of the 15th Lodi Cavalry RECo composed of 16 L6/40s was sent to Benghazi in November 1942 to operate in the Ohms sector, before being transferred to Tunisia in January 1943.

After 7 April 1943, the remnants of the Novara were regrouped with those of the Lodi participating in the last battles in Tunisia until the surrender and abandonment of Africa in May 1943.

EUROPEAN FRONT - SOUTHERN FRANCE OCCUPATION

Following the collapse of France in 1940, Italy was assigned an occupation zone in the south of the country. In 1942, the 2nd Celere Division 'Emanuele Filiberto Testa di Ferro' was sent for this purpose. Within it was the Royal Piedmont Regiment equipped in part with L6 tanks (15 tanks). The division proceeded to the occupation of the Côte d'Azur based in Nice. In addition to the Royal Piedmont, the 18th Armoured Bersaglieri Regiment was also sent to France. These, having completed their training in Pordenone in early 1943, reached France with 31 tanks, finding deployment south of Toulon in the Var region. Other units were then also sent to Corsica.

▲ Self-propelled vehicles and L6/40 tanks are landed in Libya at the beginning of the conflict. State Archives.

L6/40 LIGHT TANK LIBYA CAMPAIGN

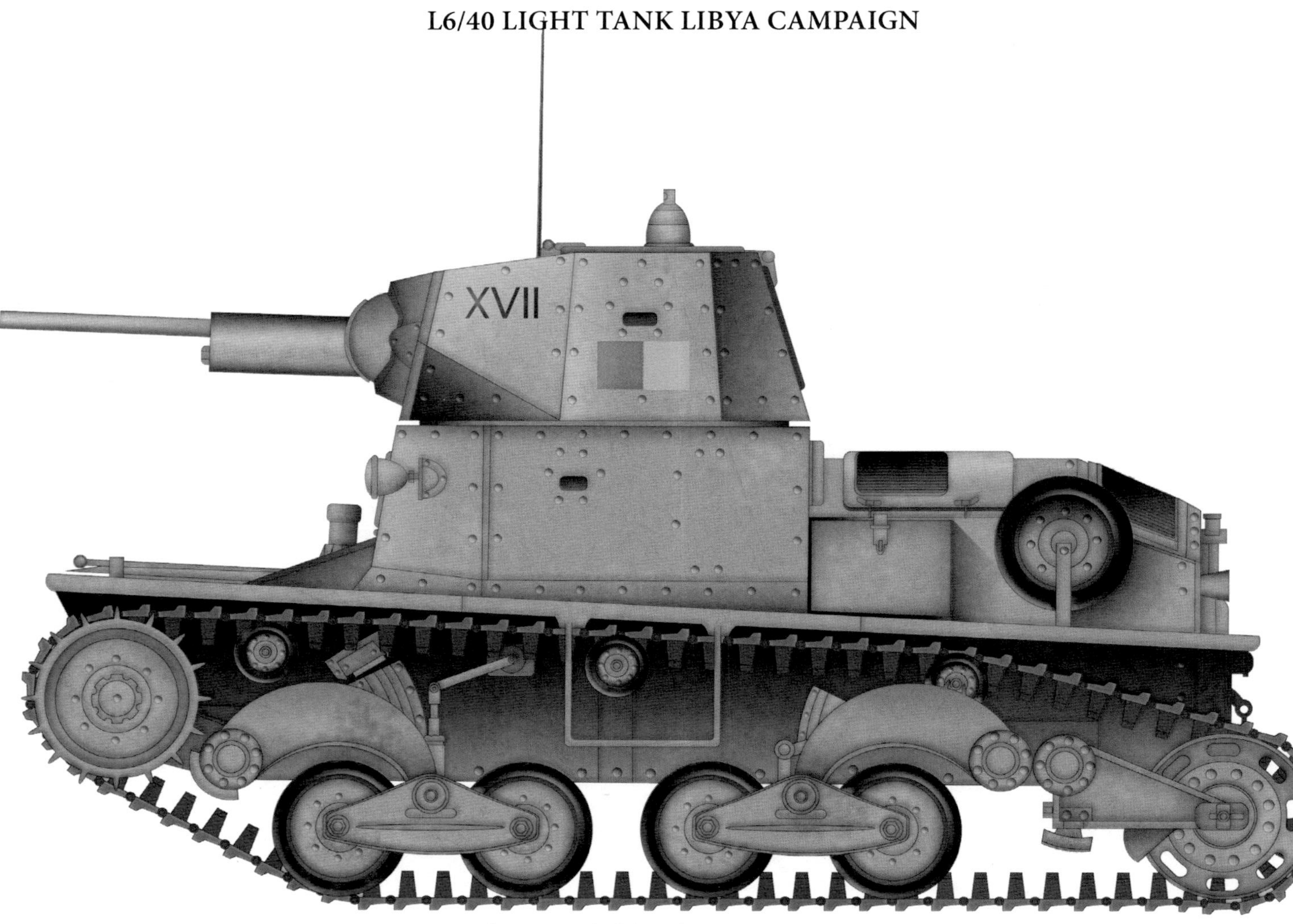

▲ 1942 L6/40 Tank Command of the 17th Light Tank Battalion in Libya, 1942.

▲ Above: L6/40 tanks of the II Gr.Cr. Novara transported to the front by Fiat 634N trucks. Below: landing of 47/32 self-propelled vehicles in a Libyan port. Small photo: two self-propelled 47/32s in action in the Libyan desert (author's colouring).

L6/40 LIGHT TANK CAMPAIGN IN NORTH AFRICA

▲ L6/40 of the 5th Lancieri di Novara Regiment. Littorio Division. North Africa Front, October 1942.

L6/40 LIGHT TANK RUSSIAN CAMPAIGN

▲ L6/40 of a Bersaglieri battalion in Italy, 1942.

RUSSIAN FRONT

Italian armoured forces were already present in 1942 within the 2ª Celere Division PADA (Principe Amedeo Duca d'Aosta). The Division's old San Giorgio Armoured Group, which had run out of tanks, was repatriated and replaced in July of the same year by the LXVII Bersaglieri Motorised Battalion, equipped with 58 L6/40 tanks, and the Alexandria Cavalry Regiment with 47 tanks and self-propelled vehicles. The first engagement took place on 27 August at Iagodniy, when nine tanks helped the Valchiese and Vestone Battalions of the 5th Alpine Regiment to repel a Soviet attack. But a few days later, one company lost 12 of the 13 tanks engaged in the space of 20 minutes under anti-tank gun fire. In December, the entire Italian front went into crisis, especially in the sector held by the Cosseria and Ravenna Divisions where the armoured grouping was stationed. On the 21st of the month, the Soviets broke through the last defences. The tanks of the LXVII Bersaglieri Battalion were almost all lost in the Gadjucja area, the rest were gradually lost during the disastrous retreat. The tanks were sent to Russia in the impractical sand painting. It was the crews who, through a thousand loopholes, managed to make the tanks more camouflaged to the Russian landscape, often with second-hand paint found who knows where.
None of the L6s engaged in the USSR returned to Italy after the rout of the ARMIR, and one of those recovered by the Russians is now on display at the Tank Museum in Kubinka, near Moscow (see pages 42 and 49).

GREEK AND BALKAN FRONT

The Balkan front was the sector in which most L6 tanks operated. Their deployment was ideal in the fight against the Yugoslav partisans. The 4th Armoured Cavalry Group of Monferrato with 30 L6/40s was deployed in Albania from 1942, with its headquarters in Berat. The III Armoured Cavalry Group of Alexandria reached Albania in May 1942 with at least one platoon of 13 L6s. They returned to Udine just over a year later. The 2nd Armoured Group of the Guide Cavalry Regiment, with 15 L6/40s, was based in Tirana in September 1942, while the 4th Armoured Group Nice Cavalry was stationed in Dibra, also in Albania, with 15 L6s and several AB41s. The 9th Autonomous Platoon equipped with L6 tanks operated

▲ L6/40 tank belonging to the 18th Armoured Bersaglieri Scout Regiment in Russia 1942. State Archives (author's colouring).

for the 11th[a] Army in Greece from April 1943. The L.Gruppo Squadroni Armorati San Giusto operated in Dalmatia from the summer of 1943, but it is not certain whether it received the L6s intended for its 3rd Squadron before the armistice. After 8 September 1943, L6s that continued to fight alongside the Germans in the Balkans were fitted with white identification stripes. After the armistice, the Wehrmacht recovered a number of L6/40s in the Balkans that continued to operate against the partisans, who in turn captured some of them. The German army also received 17 brand new L6s.

L6 TANKS AND THE CIVIL WAR

Up to the date of the armistice, a number of L6 tanks and self-propelled vehicles were present on Italian soil, either at units or in depots. These were used by the armoured and cavalry divisions of the Ariete II Division (Regio Esercito). Most of these vehicles were destroyed during the desperate defence of Rome during the days of the armistice (Porta San Paolo and other clashes). The armistice caused the Peninsula to split into two distinct realities, in the North the Italaian Social Republic, subject to German authority, and in the South the Kingdom of Italy, with units considered co-belligerent with the Allies. There are no L6 tanks in the Regio Esercito, which fought alongside the Anglo-Americans, while in the north, with the establishment of the Republican Army, allied with the Germans, they scraped the barrel in search of every possible and usable vehicle for the newly formed Italian army. However, the L6 tanks were very few in number, because during the days of confrontation with the Germans, most of them were destroyed. Many others were confiscated by the Germans themselves, but this happened mainly in the Balkan countries. In Yugoslavia, the Tito partisans themselves recovered enough of them to arm a first Yugoslav Armoured Division. Everything else that was saved of these vehicles was 'turned over' to Graziani's army. After 8 September, the available examples that were not requisitioned by the Germans were used by the following units of the Italian Social Republic: Gruppo Corazzato Leoncello - 1 example (tank); Gruppo Squadroni Corazzato 'San Giusto' - 2 examples (self-propelled); R.A.P. Raggruppamento Anti Partigiani - Gruppo Esplorante - 1/2 unit (self-propelled); I Battaglione Bersaglieri Volontari "Mussolini" - 1 unit (self-propelled); Gruppo Corazzato "Leonessa" - 5 units (4 self-propelled and 1 tank); Battaglione Lupo della Divisione X[a] Mas - 1 unit (tank).

▲ One of the Italian L6/40 tanks used in Russia and now on display in a Russian museum (plates and colours are wrong).

L6/40 LIGHT TANK RUSSIAN CAMPAIGN

▲ L6/40 LXVII Bersaglieri Battalion in Russia, restored at the Kubinka Museum after the war, with a fanciful camouflage.

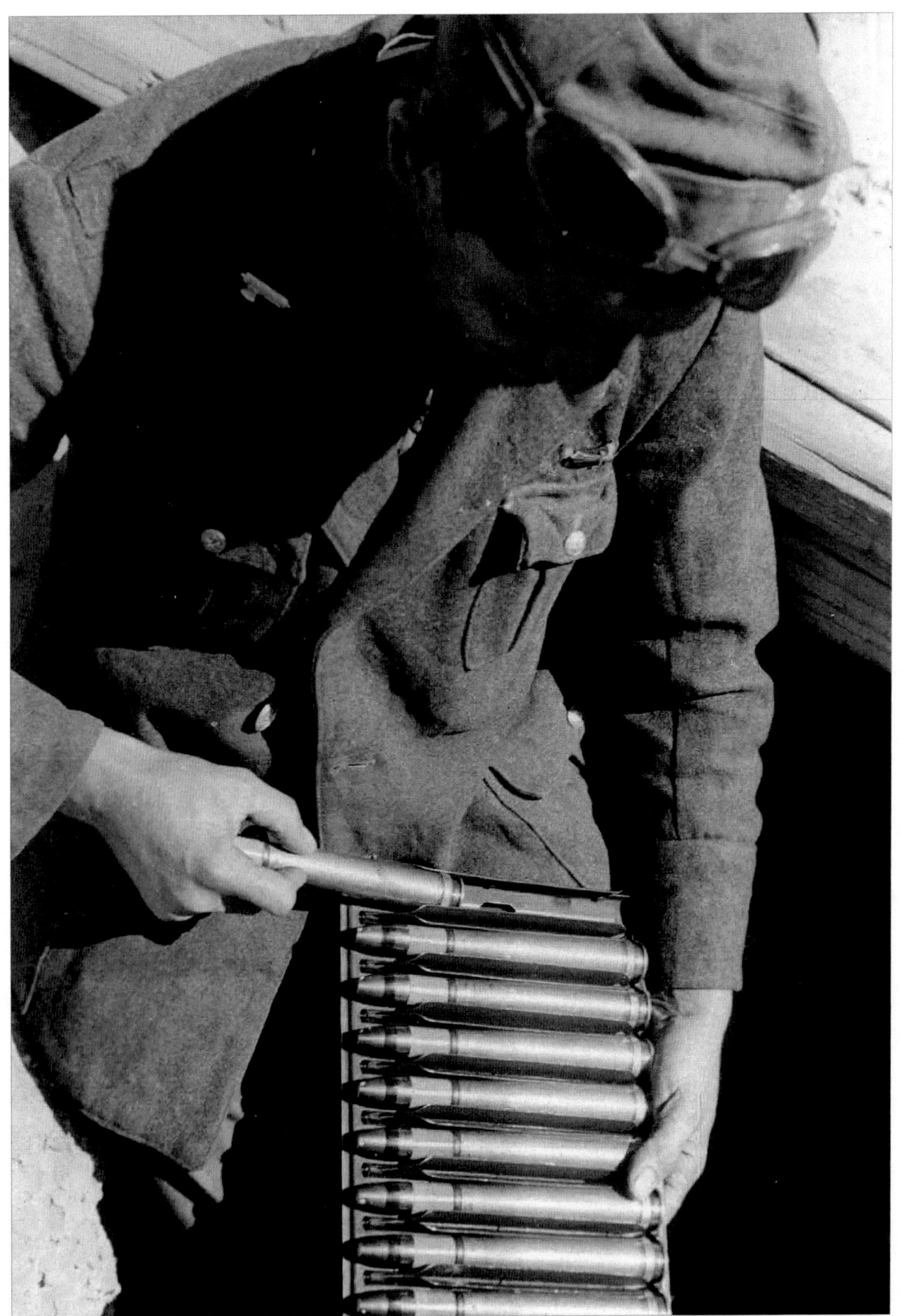

▲ An Italian soldier arms a 12-round magazine for a *Breda 20/65 Model 1935 Cannon-Mitragliera*. Libyan Desert, spring 1941. Source: Central State Archives.

THE POST-WAR PERIOD

After the war, some L6s remained with the new Italian army, and others were handed over to the Italian police force until 1952. They were used in public order operations on the occasion of the institutional referendum and various settling movements in the late 1940s. The most famous episode occurred during the so-called 'Troilus War', when P.S. officers, in war gear with L6s, garrisoned the premises of the Milan police headquarters in Via Fatebenefratelli. The Yugoslav army also kept at least three L6s in service until the early 1950s.

After the war, the L6/40 received different camouflage schemes. The vehicles given to the Milan P.S. were painted, like all post-war Italian police cars, in amaranth red, a particular shade of red that was useful for two reasons: firstly, the colour was able to cover up the previous military badges; secondly, at the time, public safety vehicles did not have sirens, so a bright red vehicle was more visible in city traffic.

► Uniform of the Italian tank drivers 1940-1943. Artwork by the author.

▲ September 1943, defence of Rome. At least four L6/40s of the 5th Battalion 'Vittorio Bòttego' on the road between Mentana and Monterotondo, together with an AB41, also of PAI, on 9 September 1943. Note the PAI initials on the left side of the cover.

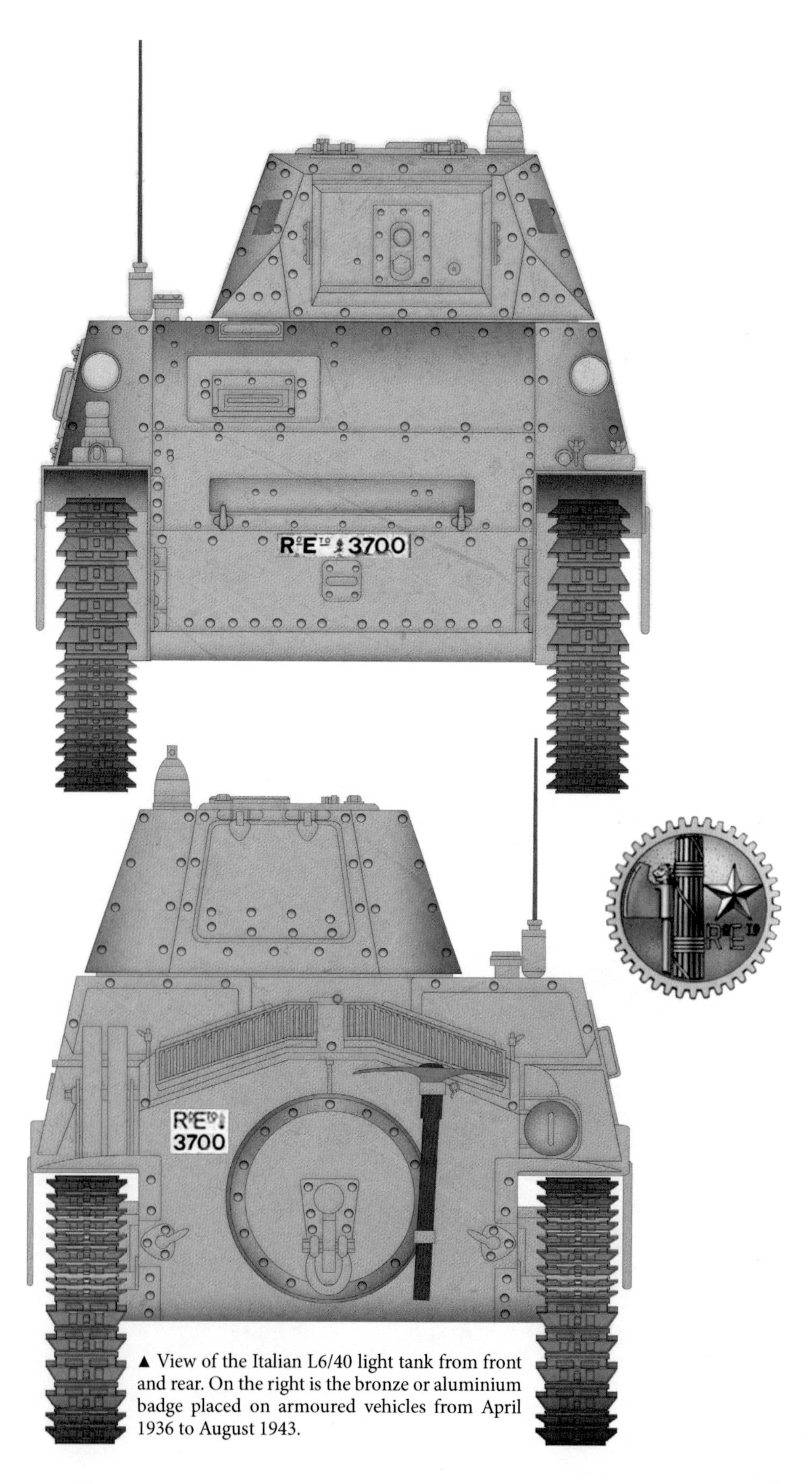

▲ View of the Italian L6/40 light tank from front and rear. On the right is the bronze or aluminium badge placed on armoured vehicles from April 1936 to August 1943.

SELF-PROPELLED 47-32 TANK TUNISIAN CAMPAIGN

▲ Semovente 47-32 deployed during the last containment campaign in Tunisia, 1942.

▲ Self-propelled L40 47/32 proceed to reoccupy the quay in the port of Bastia (State Archives).

▲ An L6/40 in the streets of Nice in 1942. Signs painted vertically on the side of the turret (State Archives).

AMMUNITION TANK FOR SELF-PROPELLED 90-53 SICILIAN CAMPAIGN 1943

▲ L40 Ammunition Tank for 90/53 Semovente in Sicily, 1943.

L6/40 LIGHT TANK (COMMAND) BALKAN WAR 1943

▲ L6/40 Tank Command of the 1st Company of the XXXI Light Tank Battalion in Yugoslavia, early 1943.

▲ L6/40 tank of the 2nd Battalion of the 31st Tank Regiment (see page 23). In the small photo: parade of tanks PzKpfw L6 733(i) in use by the German SS-Polizei Regiment in Athens, 23 May 1944. Bundesarchiv (colouring by the author).

L6/40 LIGHT TANK GERMAN EQUIPMENT BALKAN WAR 1943

▲ L6/40 with plate RE 4017 in use by an unidentified German unit. Balkans, 1943.

CAMOUFLAGE AND DISTINCTIVE SIGNS

The background colours of Italian medium and light tanks from their creation until 1945, (the operational period of this use is indicated in brackets) also used for all armoured vehicles were: R.E. grey green (1936-1945), dark chocolate (1936-1941), reddish brown (1936-1943), ochre (for prototypes), sand (1941-1945), dark sand (1943-1945), dark grey (1941-1943). For camouflage, medium green (1936-1943) and dark red (for prototypes) were used. Medium tanks had not yet been created at the time of the Ethiopian War 1935-1936 and the Spanish Civil War 1937-1939.

National territory 1936-1940 - substantial prevalence of grey-green.

Occupation of Albania and the French Front 1939-1940 - grey-green.

Campaign in Greece and Yugoslavia 1940-1941 - grey-green possibly camouflaged with green and sand-coloured flecks.

East Africa 1940-1941 - grey green or in the old Ethiopian campaign camouflage reddish brown with green spots.

North Africa 1940-1943 - at first only grey-green, the colour in which they were generally landed at destination ports, then sand colour in various variegated versions. Not used in the Russian Campaign 1941-1943.

RSI 1943-1945 dark sand colour, reddish brown with medium dense green speckling, in uniform German panzer grey colour. In particular, the tanks of the 'Leonessa' and, to some extent, the 'Leoncello' and 'San Giusto' were dark sand-coloured. I also note the presence of elaborate camouflage in irregular chequered patterns with a sandy yellow background and green and brown patches.

MEDIUM AND LIGHT TANK BADGES

In order to recognise individual armoured vehicles in military operations, even for Italy, it became necessary to introduce an identification system, also because at least initially there were no tanks with radio equipment installed. In fact, radios only began to be installed with some regularity from 1941 onwards. In the beginning, flags with red or white drapes were used for communication.
The first table of distinctive tank markings dates back to 1925 and was very complex and articulated to excess. Number groups were only introduced in 1927 after the establishment of the Tank Regiment, and new regulations were issued in 1928. In 1940, the first deliveries of M13/40 tanks finally began, which were distributed to the various armoured divisions.
The medium tanks, as was already the case with the light tanks, bore symbols identified by markings, names and numbers placed on both sides of the hull. The numbers were painted on the front of the hull plate and on both sides.
In 1938, in order to simplify recognition, a further change was made, this time a radical one: new tactical tank symbols were established. This system was also followed by the medium-sized tanks that came into being a few years later. The tank companies were represented by coloured rectangles as follows:
The first company was red, the 2nd[a] blue, the 3rd[a] yellow, the 4th[a] green; the white colour was reserved for the regimental command tanks. The insignia of the tanks and armoured cars had to be 20 x 12 cm in size and painted in the company colour.
The coloured rectangles were cut by white bars (1 to 4 rows and a diagonal for 5th platoon) and indicated the different platoons, full colour and without rows for Company Command tanks.
The rectangles of the various platoons were surmounted by an Arabic number (the colour of the company) indicating the tank in the platoon's organic formation.
These numbers had to be 10 cm high and 1.5 cm thick, and placed in the centre of the upper side of the rectangle 2 cm apart. Below the rectangle the number of the battalion to which it belonged was placed in white Roman numerals. The battalion tanks, if in reserve at Regimental level, bore instead only

COLORI E MIMETICHE REGIO ESERCITO WW2

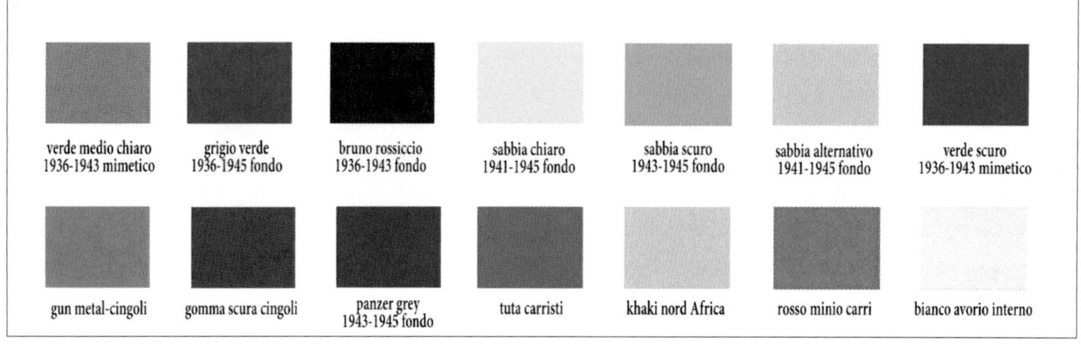

the relative Arabic number. Battalion command squadron tanks had a completely black rectangle. The battalion command tank on two companies had it half red and half blue (right). The battalion command tank on three companies had it on three coloured lines from left to right: red, blue and yellow. Specifically for the medium-sized tanks, the badge was placed on the turret in the middle front part. At the rear, in the middle part of the turret. On some tanks, the rectangle was placed at the height of the access hatch to the combat chamber. On the same hatch, the distinctive sign of the Division, such as a black ram, often appeared. As an aerial identification sign on the vehicles, a white Savoy cross was sometimes painted, in the summer of 1940, and placed on the turret or engine compartment ceiling, depending on the type of vehicle. From 1941, a white disc 70 cm in diameter was painted instead of the cross. Although the circular clearly stated, there were numerous exceptions and variations to the official regulations. The medium-sized tanks used by the Italian Social Republic showed the distinguishing marks of the various departments painted on them: the 'Leoncello' was depicted by a black lion clutching a *fascio littorio* looking to the left on a white background. The 'Leonessa' had a slightly more complicated distinguishing sign formed by the red M of Mussolini, cut by a black fasces and underneath the always black inscription 'GNR'.

The 'Leoncello' Armoured Group used, instead of coloured rectangles, a tricolour flag of the same size, with white numbering, to indicate the Squadron number (above the tricolour) and the tank number (below). The 'San Giusto' Armoured Squadron Group adopted a symbol consisting of a simple tricolour, to which the outline of a black tank was added from the spring of 1944. The tricolour was replaced later (autumn 1944) with a waving one and the silhouette of the tank with that of a self-propelled tank.

The tanks used by the Germans, especially the captured ones and the new ones ordered after the armistice of 1943, bore the typical markings of the German army starting with the black and white *ritterkreuz* in its various guises. Finally, the vehicles given to the Milan P.S. were painted like all post-war Italian police cars in amaranth red.

▲ An Italian L6/40 tank preserved at the Lubinka Museum in Russia. Already operational on the Russian front it was later captured by the Russians. Licence CC2 attributed to Alan Wilson.

L6/40 LIGHT TANK BALKAN WAR 1943

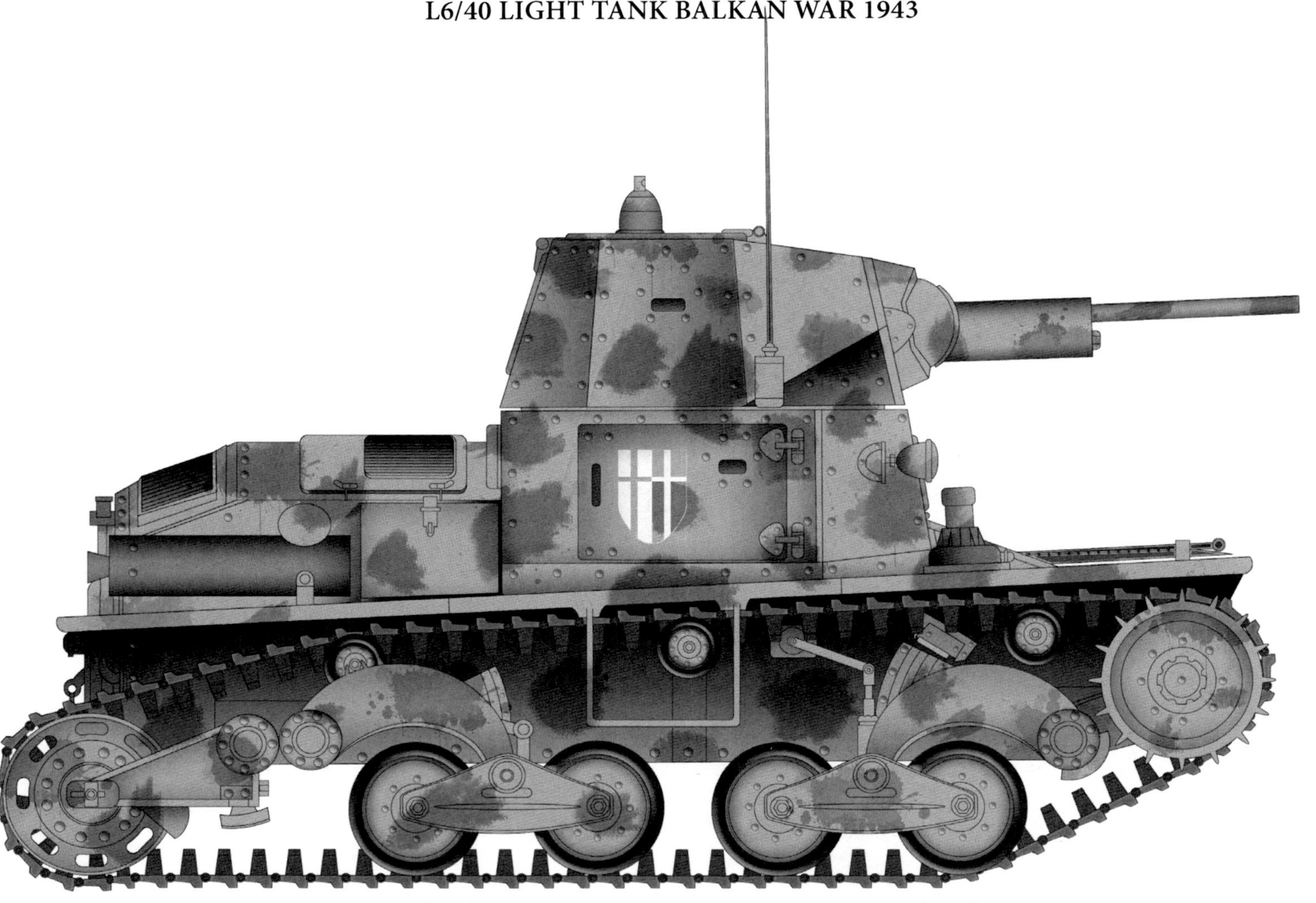

▲ L6/40 tank of the 3rd Tank Group of the Alexandria Cavalry Regiment in the Balkans, 1943.

▲▼ L6/40 tanks (above: PzKpfw L6 733(i) from a Luftwaffe unit) used by German forces. Note the adoption of the Italian helmet by the crew. Below: a German tank destroyed at Kočevje in Slovenia.

L6/40 LIGHT TANK ITALIAN CIVIL WAR 1944

▲ L6/40 tank, belonging to the 'Lupo' Battalion, 10th Mas Flotilla, RSI. Autumn 1944, Piedmont.

GERMAN L6/40 LIGHT TANK IN THE BALKANS

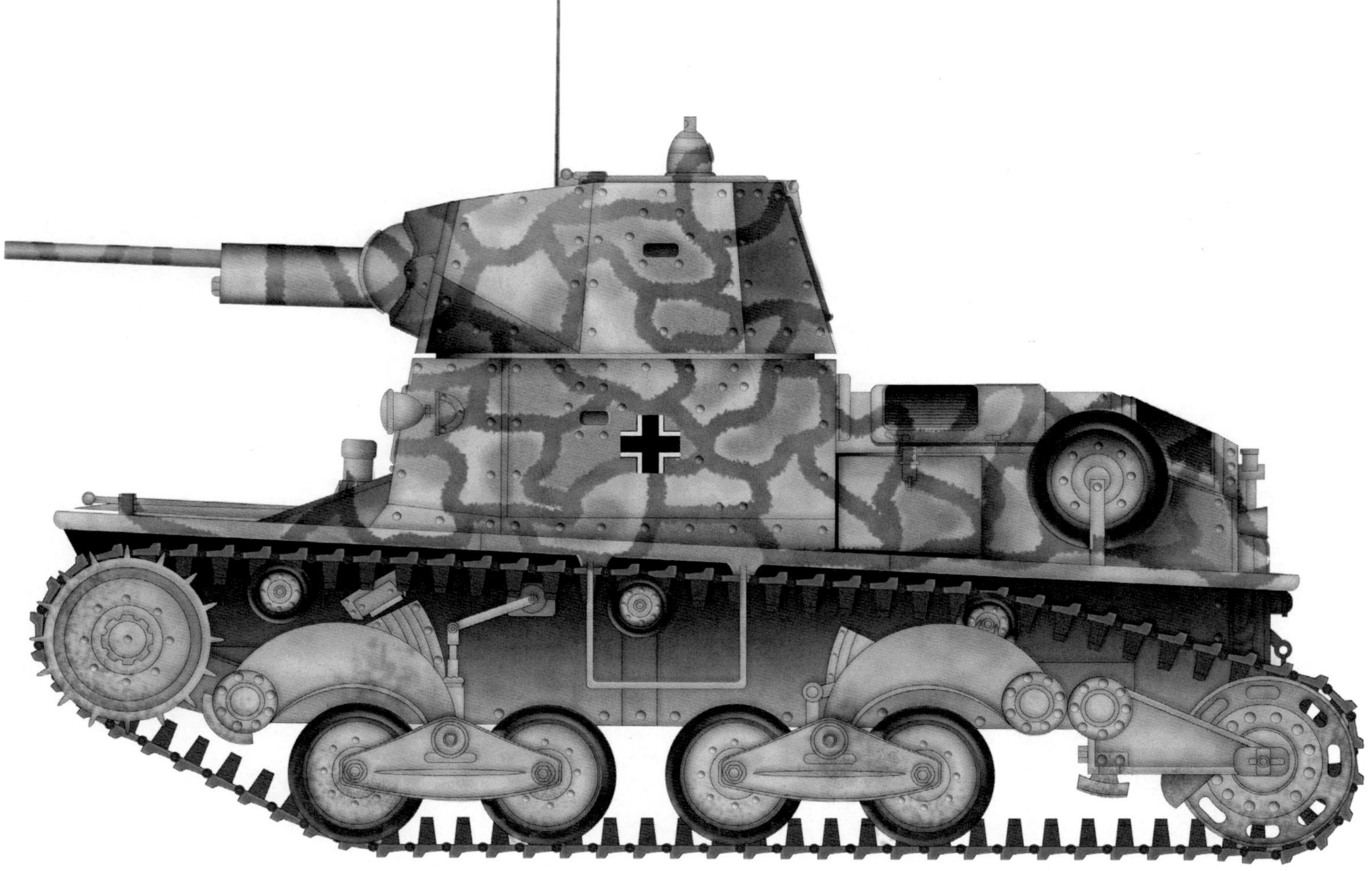

▲ L6/40 version E anti-partisan vehicle used by the Germans in the Balkans, 1944.

PRODUCTION AND EXPORT

As with many other Italian vehicles, with the possible exception of the L3 light tank, production began during wartime and there were no international markets to sell the vehicles to. The tanks, mainly due to wartime events, ended up in the usual hands of belligerent and/or allied and former allied nations.

- Royal Army: purchaser and major user of the majority of L4 armoured vehicle production in the most important versions.
- Great Britain and the Commonwealth: mainly as a result of the battles in the North African desert, British and Allied forces took possession of a number of armoured vehicles; however, there are no known re-uses of the L6/40 as, for example, happened with other Italian tank models.
- Italian Social Republic: After the collapse of Italy following the events of 8 September, a new state was created in northern Italy, controlled by the Germans. The RSI used all the military means of the Regio Esercito at its disposal and/or provided by its Germanic ally.
- German Army: In the same way, and in a massive and selective manner, the German army also confiscated and repurposed all available Italian vehicles after 8 September, in some cases even reactivating the production assembly lines (as in the case of L6 vehicles and derived self-propelled vehicles).
-

MAJOR USER

The light tank and its self-propelled version were used by the armies mentioned above, but obviously its main users were Italy and its armoured units: by the Regio Esercito above all, but also, after the Armistice, by the Esercito Nazionale Repubblicano and the Guardia Nazionale Repubblicana, following the establishment of the Italian Social Republic in 1943. However, it seems excluded that the co-belligerent Southern Kingdom used these tanks. A few vehicles were also captured in the European theatres of war, especially in Dalmatia and the Balkans; in the case of the L6/40 in particular by the Yugoslav Titin partisans. Some of these vehicles remained in service in Italy for a short time during the immediate post-war years, mainly as part of police missions.

▲ Rare example of an L4 self-propelled vehicle preserved in an American museum. Wikipedia CC1.

► A beautiful view of the L6/40 tank from above, showing the rear lines. Ansaldo source.

► L6/40 about to get on the trailer for transport. There were many tests to adapt this vehicle for transport.

▲ Top view of the L4 self-propelled vehicle hull. Photo: Fiat.

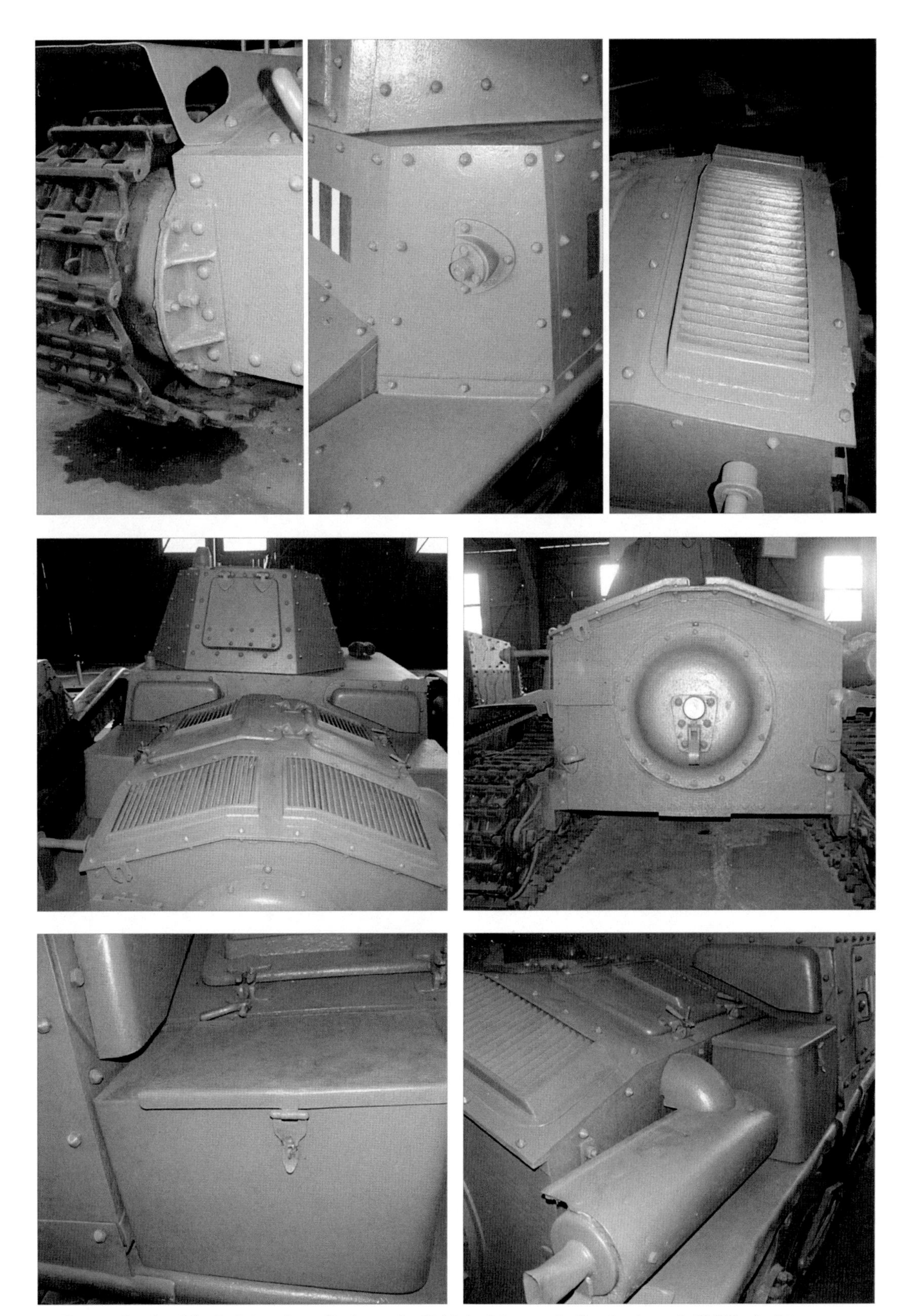

▲ Various details of the L6/40 tank on display at the Kubinka Museum in Russia. Antonio Tallillo Archive.

▲ L6/40 captured and 'decorated' by partisan formations. Paolo Crippa Archive.

▼ Two L6/40s rearmed with Breda Model 1938 twin machine guns on the streets of Milan in November 1947, engaged in the so-called Trailo war. Note the German flak covered by canvas in the foreground. P.S. Archives.

L6/40 LIGHT TANK ITALIAN CIVIL WAR 1943-45

▲ L6/40 of an unidentified unit that fought with the Germans after the Armistice in the Balkans. 1943-45.

TECHNICAL DATA		
	L6/40 tank	Semovente L40
Manufacturer	Ansaldo Fossati - Fiat	
Length	3820 mm	3820 mm
Width	1860 mm	1920 mm
Height	2200 mm	1630 mm
Setting date	1939-1942	1940
Set-up date	1952	1945
Weight	6.840 kg	6.825 kg
Crew	2	2/3
Engine	SPA 18D 4-cylinder petrol 4053 cm^3	
Power	70 hp (52 kW) 4053 cylinder capacity	
Traction	Tracks	
Maximum speed	43 km/h on road 20 km/h off-road	43 km/h on road 16 km/h off road
Autonomy	200 km on road 5 h off road	200 km
Tank capacity	165 L	165 L
Radio	RF1 CA	RF1 CA
Maximum slope	60%	60%
Frontal armour	30 mm (40mm superstructure)	30 mm
Side armour	15mm	15mm
Rear armour	15mm	15mm
Armament	1 20/65 Mod. 1935 20 mm cannon 1 Breda Mod. 38 8 mm machine gun	1 Mod. 38 47/32 cannon 47 mm. 1 Breda Mod. 38 8 mm machine gun

▲ An L6/40 is loaded onto a Fiat 634N truck (state archive, author colour).

L6/40 LIGHT TANK ITALIAN CIVIL WAR 1943-45

▲ L6/40 of the Leonessa Armoured Group. Northern Italy, 1944.

▲ ▼ Some L6/40 light tanks that ended up in the hands of the Yugoslav Titorese forces and were immediately employed in their nascent armoured formations. Paolo Crippa Archive. Author's colouring.

L6/40 LIGHT TANK ITALIAN CIVIL WAR 1945

▲ L6/40 mezzo non identificato in dotazione alla GNR RSI. Nord Italia, 1945.

SELF-PROPELLED TANK 47-32 ITALIAN CIVIL WAR 1945

▲ Self-propelled L 47 32, Tank Squadron M, Armoured Squadron Group 'San Giusto', ERN RSI. Italy, April 1945.

L6/40 LIGHT TANK POLICE SERVICE ITALY 1947

▲ 1947 L6/40 version in use at the PS celere department Milan. Italy, 1947-1948.

BIBLIOGRAPHY

- *Veicoli da Combattimento dell'Esercito Italiano dal 1939 al 1945.* Falessi, Cesare; Pafi, Benedetto (1976). Intyrama books.
- *Carro L 6, Carri leggeri, semoventi, derivati,* Andrea Tallillo, Antonio Tallillo & Daniele Guglielmi, Gruppo Modellistico Trentino, 2007
- *Carro armato L6/40* , 2007 Daniele Guglielmi. Italeri Bologna 2008
- *Carri leggeri, L.6/40 sviluppo ed operazioni, Carri Armati 2/III,* Fronte Terra, Bruno Benvenuti & Ugo F. Colonna, Edizioni Bizzarri, 1974
- *Italian light tanks 1919-1945,* Filippo Cappellano & Pier Paolo Battistelli, Osprey Publishing, 2012
- *Gli autoveicoli da combattimento dell'Esercito Italiano, Volume secondo (1940-1945),* Nicola Pignato & Filippo Cappellano, Stato Maggiore dell'Esercito, Ufficio Storico, 2002
- *La meccanizzazione dell'esercito dalle origini al 1943, Tomo II,* Lucio Ceva & Andrea Curami, USSME, 1994
- *Mezzi dell'Esercito Italiano 1935-45,* Ugo Barlozzetti & Alberto Pirella, Editoriale Olimpia, 1986
- *Italian armoured vehicles 1940-1943 : A pictorial history,* Luca Massacci, Roadrunner, 2013
- *Italian Armored Vehicles of World War Two,* Nicola Pignato, Squadron publications, 2004
- *Italian Tanks and Combat Vehicles of World War II,* Ralph Riccio, Marcello Calzolari e Nicola Pignato, Roadrunner Mattioli, 2010
- *Storia dell'Ansaldo 6. Dall'IRI alla guerra, 1930-1945,* Gabriele De Rosa, Editori Laterza, 1999
- *Storia della PAI, Polizia Africa Italiana 1936-1945,* Raffaele Girlando, Italia Editrice 2003
- *...Come il diamante, I Carristi italiani 1943-45,* Sergio Corbatti & Marco Nava, Laran Éditions, 2008
- *I reparti corazzati della Repubblica Sociale Italiana 1943/1945,* Paolo Crippa, Marvia Edizioni, 2006
- *Una visita al fronte orientale,* Daniele Guglielmi & Luca Massacci, Storia Militare n°259, 2015
- *Les véhicules blindés italiens 1910/43 (1ère partie),* Daniele Guglielmi & David Zambon, Batailles & Blindés n°24, 2008
- *Storia dei mezzi corazzati.* Pignato, Nicola. Vol. II. Fratelli Fabbri Editori.
- *I reparti corazzati italiani nei Balcani,* Paolo Crippa e Carlo Cucut. Soldiershop 2019.
- *I reparti corazzati del R.E. E l'armistizio 1° Volume,* Paolo Crippa. Soldiershop 2021.
- *I reparti corazzati del R.E. E l'armistizio 2° Volume,* Paolo Crippa. Soldiershop 2021.
- *Il gruppo corazzato del Leoncello,* Paolo Crippa. Soldiershop 2021.
- *I mezzi blindo-corazzati italiani 1923-1943,* Nicola Pignato, Storia Militare, 2005.
- *Corazzati Italiani 1939-1945,* Nico Sgarlato, War Set n°10, 2006.
- *Corazzati e blindati italiani dalle origini allo scoppio della seconda guerra mondiale,* David Vannucci, Editrice Innocenti, 2003.

AVAILABLE TITLES OF THE SERIE (ENGLISH OR ITALIAN EDITION)

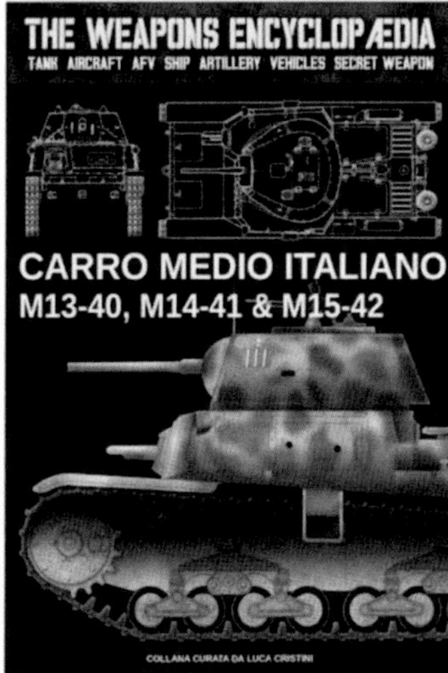

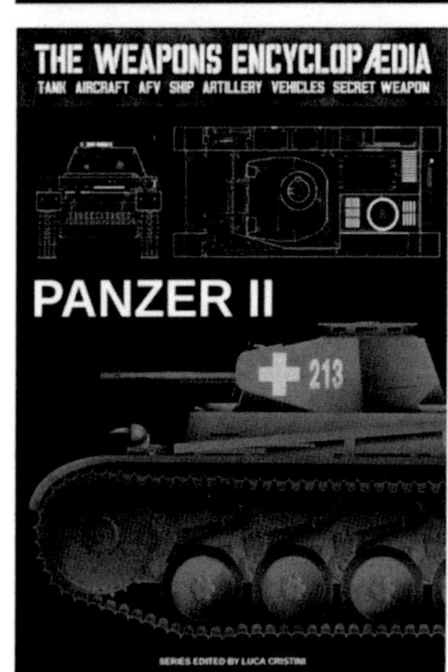

SOLDIERSHOP
PUBLISHING
ILLUSTRATED HISTORY
TWE-010 EN

Made in United States
Orlando, FL
03 March 2024